CRAIG AND HIS MAGICAL BASKETBALL

Craig Smith
Black Rhino Creative

CRAIG AND HIS MAGICAL BASKETBALL
by Craig Smith

Published by Black Rhino Creative
14320 Ventura Blvd. #440
Sherman Oaks, CA 91423

ISBN 979-8-218-06488-4 (Paperback)

Illustrations by Muhammad Asif Bhutta
Cover and interior design by Hansel Noriega

Acknowledgments

I would like to thank my mother, Linda, for putting the basketball in my hands and inspiring me to go after my dreams. I would also like to thank all those who have helped me achieve my goal of becoming an NBA player — I'm thankful for you all. And thanks to Nancy Sayles for her publishing and PR expertise, graphic design whiz Hansel Noriega and incredible illustrator Muhammad Asif Bhutta for making my book dream a reality. I truly appreciate it.

Craig Smith

There once was a kid named Craig. Craig had quite an imagination, and when he went on his walks to the park with his mom Linda, he often daydreamed about what he would be when he grew up.

On this particular walk to the park, Linda brought along a basketball.

When they reached the basketball court, Linda handed Craig the ball.

Craig looked down at the basketball and realized that holding this round object in his hand felt great and that whatever this game was that she was introducing him to, he was going to enjoy it. That afternoon, Linda taught Craig how to play basketball.

Linda blocked shots, showed her son a pretty amazing left-handed jump shot and she grabbed all the rebounds. When the game was over, Craig felt like he had just been given a triple scoop of his favorite ice cream on a cone!

On the walk back home, Craig could not let go of the basketball. The way he just played made it feel so natural and freeing. When Craig looked down at the ball, he couldn't believe what he was seeing. The ball started to glow!

Craig yelled out to his mom, “Do you see the basketball? It’s glowing!”

Even though Craig's mom couldn't see the glow herself, she felt his excitement for the game.

Linda was happy that her son had found his dream — something that he truly loved to do. After that day, Craig went to the park every day to play basketball. Even when his mom could not go, he would invite a friend.

The more Craig played, the more the ball glowed. One day, Craig went up against some local kids who were playing at the park. These kids were older and bigger, so Craig was a little nervous at first. Craig heard his mom's voice in his head telling him, *"Don't let them push you around. They will make you better!"*

Craig stayed in the game. He felt the older kids were testing him, but he knew he had something special and he never let them beat him! After this game, he finally knew what his destiny was — he was going to play in the NBA!

With such a long way to go, Craig knew that he had to perfect his game. He knew that with lots of practice and hard work, he could accomplish his dreams. *But how am I going to do that?* he wondered. So Craig went to his mom and told her that basketball was exactly what he had been searching for, and more than anything, he wanted to get better.

Linda quickly signed Craig up for any local teams she could find to help him play his very best. Craig was so excited, he just couldn't wait to get started!

As Craig grew, his game got better and better. Soon, he started to get noticed by coaches from something called the Amateur Athletic Union, or AAU. They had watched him play and wanted to have him play on their teams. Craig jumped at the chance and was signed up to play on a team called Top Prospects.

When Craig started to go to practices, he noticed that he had some real competition, so he worked and worked to show he was good enough to play with these guys.

Even though Craig had gone up before against guys who were bigger and better, he knew this would be harder because he was playing against the very best guys not only in the city, but the state and even the whole country! After being on the team for a while, everything was going well until one game that changed everything.

That was the day that Craig learned it was not the *team's* fault when he had to sit on the bench, *he* was the one who needed to be a better teammate! And you know what? From that day on, he was! Craig understood he should cheer his team on even when *he* wasn't playing. Especially on the days Craig sat on the bench or when he had a tough game, the coach would see he supported all of the guys, all of the time. That way, the coach was sure to see Craig was a real team player.

Craig understood that he would need to put in extra work if he wanted the chance to play more, and he learned that if he was always ready, he could take anything on!

But when game day came, Craig could not find his magic basketball — the reason he started loving the game, wanting to play in the NBA, and why he played so well! Without it, *what could he do?* After looking for hours, Craig had to leave for the game without his magic ball.

During the game, Craig was so nervous! He thought he would never be able to play without his magic ball! After a few minutes, though, Craig was so into the game and was playing so well, he forgot all about his magic ball!

After winning the game, Craig went home and found his magic basketball! This time, however, when Craig grabbed the ball, it didn't glow! At first, Craig was really upset and thought that without his magic ball, he would not be able to win anymore, but in that split second, he realized that he had just won a game *without* it! Craig soon realized that the magic ball glowed to give him confidence and show him that he was on the right path to playing in the NBA, but the *real* hard work and drive were actually in *him*, not the ball! The magic ball was his push to go after his dream!

During the next few days, Craig hoped to see the magic ball glow once more, but it never did. Craig finally accepted that the ball would never glow again and that the magic was actually inside of *him* all along! Craig made a promise to himself, from that day forward, that he would glow just like the ball so that he could show everyone what he was made of!

3
2
1

It was then Craig realized that his dream
had actually come true!

This is a story about a kid who found his life's passion, worked hard, overcame obstacles and succeeded in fulfilling his ultimate goal to be a professional basketball player!

And you know what? When you discover what *you* want to do, you can work hard like Craig and make *all* your dreams come true too!

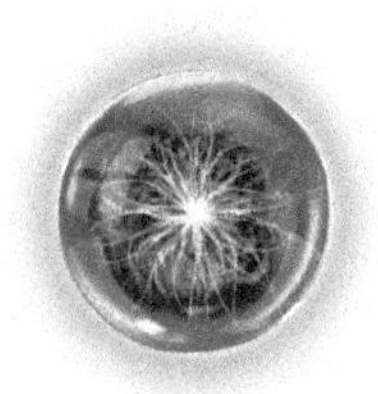

A little about Craig Smith...

As Craig entered the 9th grade, he already had years of playing under his belt. He was talented and a true student of the game, but he was at that place where he knew he had to step up his game even more. Craig attended all his practices and even played when he didn't have games. What else could he do? One morning he watched his mom wake up at 5 a.m. to get ready for work like she always did, but this morning felt different.

His mom got up early and Craig felt the need to get up early too. He would get to Fairfax High School at 6 a.m. and get his shots up. He would sweat profusely, then head to class, play during lunch, finish out the rest of his classes, play again after school, then head to practice!

Craig felt that if he was always at his best, he could get the chance to play and improve his skills at the same time. After years of practice, traveling teams, and lots of hard work, Craig went on to play basketball in college.

And then, on one very special day, he was drafted into the NBA!

I hope you can take the story of *Craig and his Magical Basketball* as an inspiration to achieve your own dreams. *Anything* is possible!

BLAZERS
MINNESOTA
5

Printed in the USA
CPSIA information can be obtained
at www.ICGtesting.com
LVHW071215290923
R17906700001B/R179067PG759079LVX00002B/1